Practice Papers
for Level One
Adult Numeracy Tests

This pack has been written by
Felicity Brasier
with contributions from Christine Harrison

edited by Marion Gibbons

The pack includes:
short individual practice papers on specific topics
covered in the national test papers

Printed October 2004
Reprinted July 2008
Reprinted March 2009

ISBN: 978 1 898614 95 1

Leading learning and skills

Introduction
Practice Papers
for Level One Adult Numeracy Tests

Family Learning courses are run in schools by Family Learning tutors for parents and carers. The courses frequently offer accreditation to the learners.

This pack contains a variety of practice test papers on individual topics that could be used after teaching to assess whether the learner has the right level of understanding for that particular section of the test.

Time limits have not been set for these papers but tutors may wish to consider timing learners to give a further feeling of a test situation.

The pack covers a range of underpinning skills from the Adult Numeracy Core Curriculum, eg:

- N1/L1.7   work out simple ratio and direct proportion
- N2/L1.9   find simple percentages
- MSS1/L1.3   calculate using time
- HD1.L1.1   extract and interpret information

Contents
Practice Papers
for Level One Adult Numeracy Tests

Multiple Choice Level 1 Numeracy Tips

- You have 40 questions and $1\frac{1}{4}$ hours in which to answer them - that is just under two minutes per question. Keep an eye on the time!!

- Do not think for too long over any one question. Either move on and go back to it or give as good a guess as you can and then go back to it.

- You have four choices of the answer to each question.

- Look at the question and think of the answer yourself - then check the answers given to see if one is the same.

- If you cannot find the answer straight away, look at the answers given in turn and see if they make sense.

- You can usually rule out two of the answers. If you are then guessing, you have a 50% chance of getting the right answer.

- Either way, do not leave an answer blank. You have a 1 in 4 chance of making the right guess!!

- Check that you understand how to mark the correct answer and how to change it. Be careful: if you change once, you cannot go back to your original answer.

- The answer sheets are computer marked - the computer will not take time to try and work out what you mean.

- Be careful that the mark you are putting on the sheet is in the correctly numbered line for the question you are answering, and that you have one answer and one answer only in each line.

Adult Numeracy Level 1
4 Rules in Everyday Life Situations

1   Tins of meat are '3 for the price of 2' at the shop. A customer was expecting to pay £1.36 for one tin. If she buys 3 tins at the offer price how much will she save per tin?

        A   £4.08
        B   45p approx
        C   £1.36
        D   90p approx

2   A special toner cartridge needs replacing every 8000 copies. Last year 25 cartridges were used at a cost of £20 each. How much did the toner cost per copy?

        A   £500
        B   2.5p
        C   0.25p
        D   £2.50

3   Every day of a year I buy a chocolate bar. If the total cost for the year is £168 (approx) which calculation will be best to work out the approximate cost per bar in pence?

A $\dfrac{168}{52}$ B $\dfrac{365 \times 168}{100}$

C $\dfrac{168 \times 100}{365}$ D $\dfrac{168 \times 100}{12 \times 52}$

4   The supermarket are giving 5p off each litre of fuel, which is currently priced at 120.9p a litre, if you spend more than £50 in the store. If you buy 30 litres at the reduced price how much will you be saving?

      A   £15
      B   £1.50
      C   £0.15
      D   77.9p

5   The table shows prices for entry to a County Show.

Adults (over 16)	£9
Children (5 – 16)	£4.50
Senior Citizens	£4.50
Family ticket – 2 adults and 2 children	£22.50
Children under 5	FREE
Car parking per car	£5

How much will it cost for Mum (35), Gran (68), Twins Jodie and Jake (10) and 5 year old Jessica if they go by car?

      A £27
      B £27.50
      C £32
      D £36.50

6   Strawberry pickers are paid £6.20 an hour. If 20 pickers are employed for 6 hours on a Tuesday how much is paid in wages in total?

      A £744
      B £492
      C £730
      D £350

7   Paula received several gifts for her birthday – they included 3 book tokens of £10 each, a Smiths token for £15, and £35 in cash. If she buys books at the local (not Smiths) bookshop for a total of £42 how much cash will she have left?

      A   £3
      B   £38
      C   £23
      D   £42

8   A man has a council tax bill of £970 per annum, to be paid in 10 equal monthly instalments starting in April. In which months will he not have to pay?

      A   January and February
      B   February and March
      C   March and April
      D   April and May

9   James was born on Thursday 5 August 20 years before his son who was born in 2003. James was asked to write his date of birth in the following box.

D	D	M	M	Y	Y	Y	Y

He should write

      A   05 08 2003
      B   5 8 1983
      C   5 08 1983
      D   05 08 1983

10   A family is planning a journey from East Anglia to
      Cornwall. They know it will be approx 400 miles, and they
      reckon on an average speed of 55 ……

      Is this speed expressed in

            A   mpg
            B   mph
            C   kph
            D   hpm

Adult Numeracy Level 1
Area and Volume

7 m

1

5 m

The area is to be covered with square tiles with sides of 0.5 m.

How many tiles will be needed?

A   35
B   140
C   70
D   48

2

100 cm

35 cm

The area of the shape is:

A 350 cm^2
B 270 cm^2
C 0.35 m^2
D 3.5 m^2

3   A path is laid using square slabs with sides of 35 cm. The path is 7 m long and 3 slabs wide. How many slabs are needed?

       A   20
       B   21
       C   63
       D   60

4   A carpet is needed for a room 4.5 m long and 2.5 m wide. The area of the carpet is:

       A 10.25 m^2
       B 11.25 m^2
       C 12.25 m^2
       D 9.25 m^2

5   Part of a bathroom wall is to be decorated with tiles measuring 25 cm x 25 cm. The area to be covered measures 2 m x 3 m.

How many tiles will be needed?

       A   24
       B   48
       C   72
       D   96

6   The area of a rectangle is 12 000 m². If the length is 400 m how wide is it?

      A   30 m²
      B   300 m²
      C   30 m
      D   11 600 m

7   A box has bars of chocolate in it. The bottom layer has 6 rows of 3 bars, and there is room for 10 layers. How many bars of chocolate will fill the box?

      A   180
      B   28
      C   19
      D   120

8   A garden bed is 5 m x 2.62 m. What is the area?

      A   7.62 m²
      B   131.0 m²
      C   13.1 m²
      D   5.24 m²

9

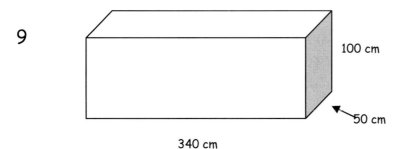

100 cm

50 cm

340 cm

What is the volume of the box?

      A   170 000 cm³
      B   1 700 000 cm³
      C   750 000 cm³
      D   1 700 000 cm²

Adult Numeracy Level 1
Averages

1   In a 'Guess the weight of the cake' competition 7 people make the following guesses:

Weight of the cake in kg - estimates						
3.5	4.35	2.65	4	3.63	2.05	3.62

What is the average (mean) estimate of the weight?

     A   3.4 kg

     B   3.62 kg

     C   4 kg

     D   3.5 kg

2   What is the range of the guesses?

     A   2.05 kg

     B   4.35 kg

     C   2.3 kg

     D   0.12 kg

3   A man swims every day on holiday in the hotel pool, and keeps a record of the number of minutes he swims, and the daily temperature.

	Sun	Mon	Tues	Wed	Thurs	Fri	Sat
Length of swim in minutes	45	52	45	44	45	58	40
Pool temperature in °C	18	19	17	17	18	18	17

What is the average (mean) amount of time that he swims each day?

A   45 min

B   46 min

C   47 min

D   48 min

4   What is the range of the temperature of the water?

A $2^{\circ}C$

B $19^{\circ}C$

C $17^{\circ}C$

D $17.5^{\circ}C$

5   Which calculation gives the mean average of the water temperature?

A $\dfrac{17 + 17 + 17 + 18 + 18 + 18 + 19}{7}$

B $\dfrac{7}{18 + 19 + 17 + 17 + 18 + 18 + 17}$

C $19 - 17$

D $(18 + 19 + 17 + 17 + 18 + 18 + 17) - 7$

Adult Numeracy Level 1
Estimating and Rounding

1   The height of a mountain is 7 238 m. How high is this to the nearest 10 m?

         A   7 200
         B   7 230
         C   7 240
         D   7 300

2   The number of people at a stadium is 14 000 to the nearest 1000.

     What is the largest possible number of people at the match?

         A   14 499
         B   13 900
         C   14 900
         D   14 500

3   . . . .and what is the smallest possible number on the same basis?

         A   14 000
         B   13 000
         C   13 500
         D   13 501

4   Tiles cost £10.99 a square metre, and 66.75 m² needs to be covered.

Which of these calculations will give the best estimate of the cost?

    A   £10 x 67
    B   £11 x 66
    C   £11 x 67
    D   £10 x 66

5   Which estimation would you use to check that
377 x 244 = 91988

    A   300 x 200
    B   400 x 200
    C   400 x 250
    D   300 x 300

6   In a relay race the 4 athletes in the team clock the following times for each leg of the race – 14.21 secs, 13.92 secs, 14.0 secs and 13.81 secs. What is the total time for the team correct to the nearest tenth of a second if the total time correct to the nearest hundredth of a second is 55.94 secs?

    A   55 secs
    B   55.9 secs
    C   56 secs
    D   55.8 secs

7   An approximate answer to 266.7 ÷ 3.5 is

        A   7
        B   70
        C   700
        D   7 000

8   After 15 years a car has travelled 123 456 miles. What is this to the nearest 1000 miles?

        A   123 000
        B   123 500
        C   124 000
        D   120 000

9   A water meter shows the following:

6	7	8	.	5	1

What is the reading to the nearest whole number?

        A   677
        B   678
        C   679
        D   680

Adult Numeracy Level 1
Fractions (mostly!)

1 114 meals were served at one café. $^2/_3$ of them were served after 2.00 pm. $^2/_3$ of 114 is

        A   57
        B   38
        C   76
        D   63

2 What is one third of £24?

        A   £16
        B   £8
        C   £13
        D   £12

3 One box of fertiliser improves 12 square metres of garden. How much would $\frac{3}{4}$ of a box improve?

        A   8 m^2
        B   9 m
        C   10 m
        D   9 m^2

4 60% of children had over half their maths problems correct, but 40% had less than half correct. What is 40% as a fraction?

        A $^4/_{100}$
        B $^4/_{10}$
        C $^1/_{40}$
        D $^{10}/_4$

5   36 passengers applied for a refund but only $^4/_9$ of them received it. How many did not receive it?

        A   18
        B   16
        C   20
        D   24

6   26 bulbs from a batch of 50 did not grow. What percentage is this?

        A   26%
        B   25%
        C   50%
        D   52%

7   . . . and what fraction did grow?

        A $^{12}/_{25}$
        B   48%
        C $^{13}/_{25}$
        D $^1/_2$

8   There were 1000 tickets to be sold for a concert. 650 were at the cheapest rate. What percentage is this?

        A   650%
        B   65%
        C   6.5%
        D $^{13}/_{20}$

9 £11.61 is to be shared between two people so that one has $^2/_3$ and the other has $^1/_3$. The one who has the larger amount gets:

    A   £3.87
    B   £7.74
    C   £5.80
    D   £5.81

10 Goods priced at £1218 are sold with a discount of $^1/_3$ in a sale. What is the discount?

    A   £809
    B   £812
    C   £406
    D   £306

11 The usual dose of a particular drug for a certain animal is 30 mg. On one occasion $^1/_5$ of the usual dose was advised. How much was this?

    A   5 mg
    B   6 mg
    C   1.5 mg
    D   0.5 mg

12   It costs £8.50 to hire a bike for a day. How much will it cost to hire 2 bikes for $1\frac{1}{2}$ days?

        A   £17
        B   £12.75
        C   £25.50
        D   £25

13    $\frac{1}{4}$ = 25% = 0.25; $\frac{3}{4}$ = 75% =

        A   0.75
        B   0.775
        C   0.075
        D   7.5

Adult Numeracy Level 1
Graphs and Charts

1   Loan Repayment Table

Amount of loan	Monthly repayments		
	Over 12 months	Over 36 months	Over 60 months
£3000	£246.50	£98.83	£75.89
£7500	£647.27	£230.52	£147.19
£10000	£852.91	£368.45	£241.50

Sheila borrows £10 000 from the bank and repays it over 3 years. How much does she have pay each month?

A   £852.91

B   £368.45

C   £241.50

D   £98.83

2   What does the chart below lack?

A   Label for the horizontal axis

B   Label for the vertical axis

C   Key

D   Title

**Colours of cars passing the house
at various times in the day**

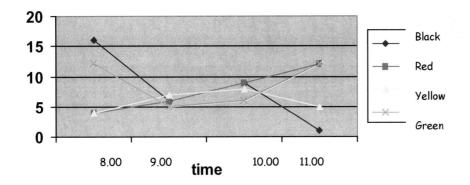

3   Match the names of these charts to the letters by
    drawing lines at the bottom of the page.

A

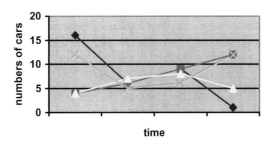

colours of cars passing the house
at various times in the day

B

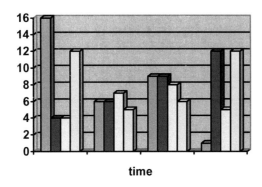

colours of cars passing the house
at various times of the day

C

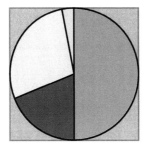

colours of cars passing the house
at various times of the day

(Match the   Pie chart   A
title to the   Line graph   B
letter here)   Bar chart   C

4   The chart for question 5 (below) is called a

      A   Bar chart
      B   Scatter graph
      C   Pictogram,
      D   Tally chart

5

Animals on Fell Farm

Ducks	
Dogs	
Horses	
Cows	
Sheep	

Key - each symbol represents 4 animals.

The number of cows on Fell Farm is

      A   6
      B   11
      C   5
      D   22

6

Chesterfield	1235	1321	1335	1351	1405	1435
Wingerworth	1249	1335	1349	1406	1419	1449
Tupton	1252	1338	1352	1409		1452

A man arrives at Chesterfield bus station at 2.00 pm.
What is the next bus he can catch to Tupton?

A   14.05
B   13.51
C   14.09
D   14.35

7

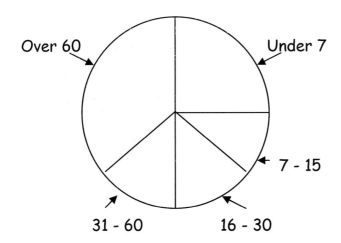

The pie chart shows the ages of the audience at a school concert. It shows that:

A The smallest group of the audience is in the Over 60 age group
B There are more 31- 60s than 16 – 30 year olds
C There are more 7 – 15 year olds that Under 7s
D There are more Under 7's than 7 – 15 year olds

8

Cambridge	286	162	749	96					
Cardiff	351	72	171	851	248				
Edinburgh	629	542	597	469	203	645			
Fishguard	737	181	513	193	285	843	418		
Glasgow	626	72	629	562	595	466	238	644	
Holyhead	514	261	523	336	396	373	248	734	425
Liverpool	170	354	268	360	320	330	285	157	581	336
Manchester	54	200	342	304	349	301	246	267	141	566	317

Above is part of a mileage chart showing the distance in kilometres between various places. How far is it from Cardiff to Liverpool?

A   301 km

B   360 km

C   320 km

D   330 km

9

Cost of tiles

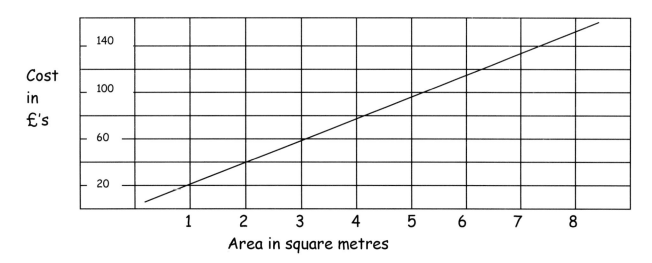

How many square metres can be covered with a budget of £120?

A Exactly 6   B Less than 6   C More than 6 D £116

Goals Scored by Town

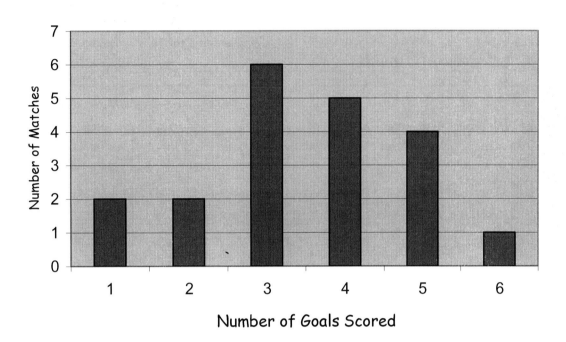

10   How many matches in total did Town play?

       A   6
       B   20
       C   5
       D   7

11   What was the maximum number of goals scored in a match?

       A   7
       B   6
       C   5
       D   4

12   In how many matches did they score more than 3 goals?

        A   6
        B   15
        C   10
        D   5

13   What was the most common number of goals?

        A   1
        B   2
        C   3
        D   6

14   A chart shows how much a school has collected towards
      its target of £4 000 for computers.

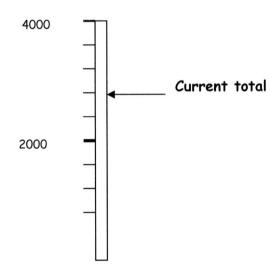

      How much has been raised so far?

        A   £2 200
        B   £2 400
        C   £2 800
        D   £3 000

Adult Numeracy Level 1
Metric Measurements

Length

1   A lawn measures 14.8 metres long by 8.3 metres wide, and the area is 122.8 square metres.
Which calculation gives the closest estimate of the area?

      A   14 x 8
      B   14 x 9
      C   15 x 8
      D   15 x 9

2   A path leads from a gate to a shed.

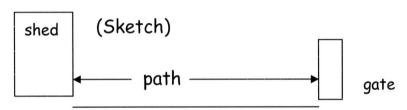

Scale to be shown as 10 mm represents 2 m

If the length of the path on the drawing is 7.2 centimetres what is the actual length of the path?

      A   14.4 cm
      B   7.2 cm
      C   14.4 m
      D   72 m

3   A set of wall panels is to be covered with an expensive paint costing £12.45 a litre. A litre will cover 12 m^2 and the total area of the panels is 214 m^2. Which calculation will give the amount of paint needed?

      A   214 ÷ 12 x 12.45
      B   12.45 x 12
      C   12 x 214
      D   214 ÷ 12

4   Diagram of a wall panel (not to scale)

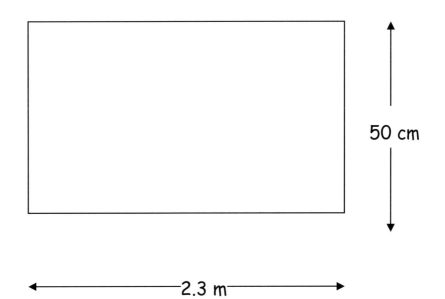

50 cm

2.3 m

What is the area of the wall panel?

A   5.6 m²
B   2.8 m²
C   115 m²
D   1.15 m²

5   A customer wanted 4 m 8 cm of material. Which arrow shows the exact amount needed?

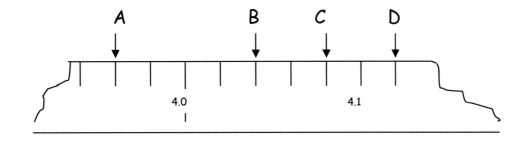

A
B
C
D

6 Unfortunately the material is only sold to the nearest
   0.5 m. How much will the customer have to buy?

      A   4.5 m
      B   4 m
      C   5 m
      D   3.5 m

7 The length of an insect is zero point three centimetres.
   Zero point three centimetres can be written as

      A   0.03 cm
      B   0.3 cm
      C   3/10 m
      D   1/3 cm

8 A carpet measures 3 metres by 5 metres. The owner says
   the area is 15 units. The units used are

      A   Metres
      B   Square metres
      C   Square centimetres
      D   Cubic metres

Weight

1. A lorry was delivering 20 sacks of coal, each weighing 50 kg. ¾ of the coal had been delivered. What weight of coal was still left on the lorry?

        A   250 kg
        B   70 kg
        C   750 kg
        D   2500 kg

2. Richard picked 2.5 kg of strawberries, Tom picked 500 g and Murray picked 1½ kg. How many 500 g containers did they fill altogether?

        A   7
        B   8
        C   9
        D   10

3. How many bags of potatoes, each weighing 3 kg, can be made from a delivery of 75 kg?

        A   225
        B   25
        C   250
        D   2.5

4. 6 tins of fruit weigh 10.2 kg. How much would 4 tins weigh?

        A   6.8 kg
        B   38.52 kg
        C   1.7 kg
        D   68 kg

5. 10 biros weigh 84 g. How much would 4 biros weigh?

        A   33.6 g
        B   8.4 g
        C   33.6 kg
        D   16.8 g

Capacity

1. Mum mixed 1.75 litres of water with $1\frac{1}{4}$ l of orange and 500 ml of lemon. She shared the drink between 7 children. How much did each child have?

 A   250 ml
 B   750 ml
 C   3.5 litres
 D $\frac{1}{2}$ litre

2. Tim mixed some water and paint. The bucket had 9.8 litres of mixture in it. He had used 4.5 litres of water. How much paint had he put in?

 A   15.3 litres
 B   15 300 ml
 C   5 300 ml
 D   5.3 litres

3. Mary fills thirty 200 ml bottles with water. How many litres of water does she need?

 A   6 litres
 B   600 litres
 C   6 000 litres
 D   60 litres

4. I bought 10 cans of drink – each can containing 160 ml. How many litres of drink had I bought?

 A   1 600 litres
 B   10 litres
 C   16 litres
 D   1.6 litres

5. What is the total of the following amounts – in millilitres?

 300 ml   1.45 litres   250 ml   1 litre 500 ml

 A   3 litres 500 ml
 B   3.5 litres
 C   3 500 ml
 D   35 000 ml

Adult Numeracy Level 1
Percentages

1 Yasmin paid £1 500 for her family's holiday. She used 50% of the money in her bank account to pay for it. How much was in her account to start with?

        A   £750
        B   £1 000
        C   £3 000
        D   £2 000

2 Out of 50 oranges 17 had labels on – what percentage is this?

        A   17%
        B   34%
        C   50%
        D   67%

3 Out of 460 people 25% like jacket potatoes. How many is this?

        A   125
        B   115
        C   230
        D   25

4 Goods are offered at a discount of 25% off the original price. If the original price was £360 how much will actually be paid?

        A   £90
        B   £335
        C   £270
        D   £250

5    $\frac{1}{4}$ = 25% = 0.25 $\frac{3}{4}$ = 75% =

       A   75
       B   0.75
       C   .075
       D   7.5

6   A survey shows how 200 people travel to work on a particular day. 21 go on foot, 90 go by car, 55 go by bus and the rest cycle. What percentage cycle?

       A   166%
       B   34%
       C   64%
       D   17%

7   At a clinic there are 50 people; 30% are female. How many are male?

       A   35
       B   45
       C   20
       D   36

8   3000 people were asked whether they use 'Bright' or 'Clean' toothpaste. 25% chose 'Clean'. How many people is that?

       A   25
       B   750
       C   1 500
       D   250

9   5% is to be added to the original quote for a driveway. The original quote was £2 200. How much will actually have to be paid?

A   £2 420
B   £2 250
C   £2 700
D   £2 310

10   A bottle of squash is 60% full. What fraction has been used?

A $^6/_{10}$
B $^2/_5$
C $^3/_5$
D $^3/_8$

11   120 people were at a concert. 20% had concessionary tickets. How many people was this?

A   20
B   12
C   40
D   24

12   40% of the apples on the tree were bruised. What fraction is this?

A $^1/_{40}$
B $^2/_5$
C $^4/_{100}$
D $^1/_4$

13   6 out of the 30 people taking a test were late in arriving. What % is this?

        A   6%
        B   5%
        C   20%
        D   25%

14   The pass mark for a test is 29 out of 40. Which of the following gives the % needed to pass?

        A $\dfrac{29}{40} \times 100$ B $\dfrac{29}{100} \times 40$

        C $\dfrac{29}{100 \times 40}$ D $\dfrac{40}{100} \times 29$

15   A house was valued at £100 000 in 2000, but at £126 000 in 2004 – a rise of 26%. Which calculation will check this?

        A   26% of £126 000 then + £100 000
        B   26% of £126 000 then add £126 000
        C   26% of £100 000 then add £126 000
        D   26% of £100 000 then add £100 000

Adult Numeracy Level 1
Place Value and Rounding

1   207 100 in words is

      A   Two million, seven thousand and one hundred
      B   Two million seventy-one hundred
      C   Two hundred and seven thousand one hundred
      D   Two hundred thousand seven hundred and ten

2   Round 7 624 948 to the nearest one hundred thousand.

      A   7 600 000
      B   7 700 000
      C   7 620 000
      D   7 630 000

3   Write in figures three hundred and sixty thousand and thirty-six.

      A   30 060 036
      B   36 036
      C   360 036
      D   310 036

4   The sale price of a table and chairs is £276.645 and is 18% less than the original price. Round the sale price to the nearest penny.

      A   £276
      B   £277
      C   £276.60
      D   £276.65

5   Round £0.3765 to the nearest penny.

        A   £0.37
        B   £0.38
        C   £0.376
        D   £0.377

6   47p =

        A   £47.00
        B   £0.47
        C   £04.70
        D   £40.07

7   Which is the smallest number out of the following?

        A   0.2
        B   0.20
        C   0.02
        D   0.002

8   Which number is the largest of the following?

A   Seven hundred and sixty thousand, five hundred and eight

B   Seven hundred and sixteen thousand, eight hundred and five

C   Seven hundred and sixty-two thousand, five hundred and six

D   Seven hundred and six thousand, eight hundred and five

9   Which of the following lists shows numbers in correct
     order from smallest to largest?

        A   0.001   0.02   0.1   2.10
        B   0.02   0.003   0.04   0.005
        C   0.01   0.1   0.02   0.3
        D   0.101   0.103   0.303   0.301

10   What is the total of £435, £44.65, £435.06 and £4.35?

        A   £1 320.91
        B   £1 752.10
        C   £1 360.60
        D   £919.06

Adult Numeracy Level 1
Ratio

1   Fertiliser is added to water in the ratio of 2 drops for every 25 ml of water. How many drops will be needed for a litre of water?

        A   8
        B   80
        C   25
        D   50

2   32 boys and 8 girls join a football club. The ratio of girls to boys is

        A   4:1
        B   5:1
        C   1:4
        D   1:3

3   In another club there are 24 children with a ratio of boys to girls of 5 : 3. How many girls are there?

        A   3
        B   10
        C   6
        D   9

4   Fruit squash is added to water in the ratio 1 : 4. If 0.6 litres of squash is used how much drink will be made?

        A   2.4 litres
        B   3.0 litres
        C   5.6 litres
        D   5.4 litres

5   15 kg of cement is used for every 60 kg of sand in a certain mixture. If there is 60 kg of cement how much total mixture can be made?

        A   75 kg
        B   150 kg
        C   300 kg
        D   450 kg

Adult Numeracy Level 1
Time

1   A sports programmes starts at 1.05 pm and runs for $2\frac{1}{2}$ hours. What time will it finish?

       A   3.30 pm
       B   3.35 pm
       C   3.05 pm
       D   2.30 pm

2   This is part of a public transport timetable.

Chesterbury	0620	0645	0735	0850
Langton	0630		0745	0900
Wingerpool	0634	0659	0749	0904
Tupton	0637		0752	0907
Claxborough	0703		*	0933

What time would you expect the 0735 bus from Chesterbury to reach Claxborough?

       A   0826
       B   0778
       C   0833
       D   0818

3   A man needs to get to work in Tupton by 9.10. It takes him 12 minutes to walk from the bus station to his place of work. What is the latest bus he can catch from Langton?

       A   0735
       B   0900
       C   0752
       D   0745

4   A woman misses the quarter to seven bus from Chesterbury by four minutes. How long will she have to wait for the next bus to Wingerpool?

    A   0735
    B   50 minutes
    C   46 minutes
    D   35 minutes

5   Both hands on a clock are pointing to the 12. How many minutes will have passed when the big hand is next pointing to the 11?

    A   5
    B   50
    C   55
    D   11

6   How many minutes are there between a person going to bed at 11.56 pm, and having lunch at 1.30 pm the next day?

    A   94
    B   814
    C   694
    D $13\frac{1}{2}$ hours

Answers to Adult Numeracy Level 1

Level 1   4 Rules in Everyday Life Situations

1	B
2	C
3	C
4	B
5	C
6	A
7	C
8	B
9	D
10	B

Level 1   Area and Volume

1   B; A is the answer if the tiles were 1 m square, C is A doubled; D is perimeter doubled.

2   C; A is 35 x 10; B is the perimeter but written as cm^2, D is C x 2.

3   D; A is the number of slabs in 7m. ; B is 7m x 3 slabs; C is approx 3 slabs to each metre length x 3.

4   B: the rest are due to inaccurate multiplication.

5   D; A would be the answer if the tiles were 50cms square – the others lie in between A and D.

6   C; A is square metres, B is a mistake in x/÷ 10 etc, D is a subtraction.

7   A; B is 6 x 3 + 10; C is 6+3+10; D is inaccurate multiplication.

8   C; A is addition; B has the decimal point in the wrong place; D doubles. NB It would probably be quickest to x 10 and ÷ 2)

9   B; A has x by 10 instead of 100; C has added various lengths; D is cm^2.

Level 1   Averages

1	A
2	C
3	C
4	A
5	A

Level 1   **Estimating and Rounding**

1   C
2   A
3   C
4   C
5   C
6   B
7   B
8   A
9   C

Level 1   **Fractions (mostly)**

1   C: A is ½, B is $^1/_3$ and D is a guess at more than ½
2   B: A is 2/3, D is ½, and C misuses the figures given
3   D: A is 2/3, B is correct figure but in metres; C is incorrect figure
4   B: a simplification of $^{40}/_{100}$
5   C: B is $^4/_9$ and the others are random
6   D
7   A: B is correct as a %, C is the amount that did not grow.
8   B
9   B: A is $^1/_3$, and C and D are near halves
10   C: B is the sale price. A and D are incorrect calculations
11   B
12   C
13   A

Level 1   **Graphs and Charts**

1   B
2   B
3   A = line graph, B = bar chart, C = pie chart
4   C
5   D
6   D
7   D
8   C
9   C
10   B
11   B
12   C
13   C
14   C

Level 1   Length

1   C: question requires knowledge about rounding up and down.
2   C: this is easiest if students can recognise 10mm as 1 cm.
3   D: the price is irrelevant to the question.
4   D: A is the perimeter, B is half the perimeter, C multiplies but mistakes cm for m.
5   C: need to recognise that 10 cm = 0.1 m, and 1 cm = 0.01m.
6   A: no good having too little!
7   B
8   B

Level 1   Weight

1   A
2   C
3   B
4   A
5   A

Level 1   Capacity

1   D
2   D
3   A
4   D
5   C

Level 1   Percentages

1   C: A is 50% of the original; B subtracts £500 from the original; D adds £500 to the original.
2   B: A is number rather than %; C takes the other number; D adds the two numbers together.
3   B: A has ÷ by 4 but inaccurately; C has ÷ 2; D takes the number.
4   C: A has quoted the actual discount; B has discounted by £25; D has found the correct discount but subtracted inaccurately.
5   B: the rest are misunderstandings of place value or %.
6   D: A is 21+ 90+ 55; B is the difference between that and 200 – ie the **number** of people who cycle; C is the number x 2 instead of ÷ 2
7   A: B has probably worked out 30% correctly but then subtracted wrongly; C is using numbers not %; D may know that 70% approx = $\frac{3}{4}$
8   B: A is using the number not the %; C ÷ 2 instead of by 4; D takes the % and adds a 0
9   D: A adds 10%; B adds £50; C adds £50.
10   B: A gives the amount left; C the same but simplified; D probably thinks that less than a half has gone.
11   D: A uses the number; B gets 10%; C probably doubles the %.
12   B: A uses the 40 at the bottom; C has the % idea; D uses the 4 in a 'known' fraction.
13   C: A uses the 6; B probably says 6 x 5 = 30; D thinks 6 is about a $\frac{1}{4}$.
14   A
15   D

Level 1   Place value and Rounding

1   C
2   A
3   C
4   D
5   B
6   B
7   D
8   C
9   A
10   D

Level 1   Ratio

1   B; A assumes there are 100 ml in a litre; C and D guess from the figures given
2   C; A is the wrong way round; B and D are guesses
3   D; A uses the figure from the ratio; B thinks it is nearly half; C doubles the 3
4   B; A has multiplied the 0.6 by 4; C and D are random guesses
5   C; A has the total for one unit of mixture, B for 2 and D for 6

Level 1   Time

1   B
2   D
3   D
4   C
5   C
              6   B

Publications by Suffolk Family Learning

All our packs are written by experienced skills for life/family learning tutors who have based the packs on courses that they have run. They contain ideas, facts, handouts and worksheets for tutors to use in workshops or courses to support learning of parents and carers.

Calculations ISBN 1 898614 59 8
Ideas for parents/carers to use calculations in everyday fun with their children. 32-page pack written by Marion Gibbons.

Chaser Cards ISBN 1 90530913 9 from 2007 978 1 90530913 9
A pack of A4 photocopiable chaser card games. The set covers literacy and numeracy with a range of topics including nouns, antonyms, addition and percentages. 40-page written by Marion Gibbons.

Creative Writing ISBN 1 898614 63 6
Enjoyable exercises to give parents and carers a chance to try out writing for themselves. 47-page pack written by Bernardine Freud.

Family Activities in Your Community ISBN 1 898614 99 7
This pack is about finding out what activities are available, in the local community, for parents/carers and their children. It looks at the skills involved in finding the information that is needed. A range of topics are covered and opportunities are provided to practise some of the skills needed in researching and participating in family activities in the community. 53-page pack written by Carol Gladstone.

Family Finance ISBN 1 898614 78 4 & ISBN 1 898614 79 2
Two packs containing a complete 30-hour course on Financial Literacy including scheme of work, session plans and handouts/worksheets course explaining some of the everyday financial terms and looking after personal money. Pack 1: 92 pages, Pack 2: 58 pages, both written by Marion Gibbons.

Fun with Food ISBN 1 898614 89 X
This pack is designed to provide suggestions and ideas for family fun and learning in the context of food. There are some games and exercises that can be done in groups or as individuals. 90-page pack written by Christine Minton and Lindsay Wolton.

Fun with Food Workshop ISBN 1 898614 97 0
19 activities and 2 ice-breakers related to food, created into workshop ideas. Every activity has a handout, learning outcomes and paper-based materials provided. In some of the activities real food will be needed for weighing, measuring, and sometimes, if appropriate, tasting. There are also games to be made. This pack could be used for tutor training to give tutors ideas, as well as for learners. 55-page pack written by Marion Gibbons.

Health Choices ISBN 1 898614 58 X
Worksheets covering the skills needed to gather information on a range of topics related to family health. 51-page pack written by Bernardine Freud and Christine Minton.

Helping in the Community ISBN 1 898614 98 9
Literacy exercises and practice forms to complete all in the context of volunteering. 47-page pack written by Carol Gladstone.

ICT and Study Skills ISBN 1 898614 64 4
Explores different aspects of ICT and suggest ways in which parents can use and improve their own computer skills while working with their children. It is a practical pack that covers topics from planning writing in Word to using the World Wide Web in user-friendly terms. 57-page pack written by Gill Johnson.

Keeping Up With the Children Literacy ISBN 1 898614 71 7
Containing a scheme of work with 6 session plans and the accompanying handouts/worksheets for a KUC course. 38-page pack written by Felicity Brasier.

Keeping Up With the Children Numeracy Pack 1 ISBN 1 898614 72 5
89-page pack written by Marion Gibbons.
Keeping Up With the Children Numeracy Pack 2 ISBN 1 898614 73 3
69-page pack written by Marion Gibbons.
These two packs contain 3 schemes of work, each with 6 session plans and the accompanying handouts/worksheets for them all, giving the experienced tutor a chance to choose one of the courses or mix and match to create an individual course. They work together and have been designed to work as a pair, each supporting the other.

Keeping Up With the Children Numeracy Complete Course Pack
ISBN 1 898614 74 1
Designed for a new or experienced tutor to pick up and run a course with. It contains a scheme of work, 6 session plans and the handouts/worksheets. 103-page pack written by Felicity Brasier and Marion Gibbons.

Measures, Shape and Space ISBN 1 898614 60 1
Facts, ideas, worksheets and handouts make up this pack. 36-page pack written by Marion Gibbons.

Neighbourhood Knowledge ISBN 1 898614 91 1
Ideas for using your neighbourhood to encourage literacy and numeracy work. 40-page pack written by Jill Harrison.

Planning for a Change in Your Neighbourhood ISBN 1 898614 90 3
Ideas to help learners make their voices heard. The pack includes guidance on using PowerPoint for presentations. 60-page pack written by Lindsay Wolton.

Playing Together ISBN 1 898614 66 0
Written to support the OCN Playing Together course, this pack contains fun ideas for structured play. 36-page pack written by Alison Elliott and Marion Gibbons.

Play and Language ISBN 1 905309 00 7
A 10-week x $1\frac{1}{2}$ hour course written with a scheme of work, session plans, handouts and ideas. This course is aimed at parents/carers of 0 - 3 year olds. 68-page pack written by Kate Germany.

Playing with Language ISBN 1 898614 80 6
A complete 30-hour course for parents and carers of 3 – 6 year olds with scheme of work, session plans, worksheets and handouts. 82-page pack written by Jill Harrison.

Playing with Numbers ISBN 1 90530906 6; 978 1 90530906 1
A complete 30-hour course for parents and carers of 3-5 year olds, promoting ways in which numbers can be introduced in everyday life. The pack includes a scheme of work, session plans, handouts and ideas. 89-page pack written by Julie Rawlins.

Practice Papers for Literacy Tests ISBN 1 898614 92 X
& ISBN 1 898614 94 6
Individual papers on a range of topics designed to give learners a taste of a real test paper, but in small chunks. Tutors requested these to supplement the whole practice test papers available from awarding bodies. Written by Jill Harrison and Eileen Richards. Level One 50-page pack. Level Two 55-page pack.

Practice Papers for Numeracy Tests ISBN 1 898614 95 1
& ISBN 1 898614 96 2
As above but for Numeracy practice. Written by Felicity Brasier and Eileen Richards. Level One 49-page pack. Level Two 48-page pack.

Reading ISBN 1 898614 67 9
Looking at the skills in learning to read and the pre-reading experience. This book gives ideas, handouts and worksheets to encourage reading. 66-page pack written by Bernardine Freud.

Solving Problems and Handling Data ISBN 1 898614 61 X
Bringing these two strands of the Numeracy strategy into a format for parents to use. 61-page pack written by Marion Gibbons.

Speaking/Listening and Reading ISBN 1 898614 65 2
The important qualities of speaking and listening are explained here together with various reading methods such as skimming. 32-page pack written by Carol Gladstone.

Sport for All ISBN 1 898614 93 8
Bringing literacy and numeracy alive through sport. 72-page pack written by Juliet Bonner and Lindsay Wolton.

Stories ISBN 1 905309 05 8; from 2007 978 1 90530905 4
Ideas for writing stories: Writing frameworks, tips and worksheets on topics such as proof-reading. 62-page pack written by Christine Minton.

Story-telling Workshops ISBN 1 90530911 2; 978 1 90530911 5
A pack of ideas and handouts, based on story-telling, for use in workshops and as part of a course. 69-page pack written by Juliet Bonner.

Supporting your Children's Literacy Skills ISBN 1 898614 68 7
Progression routes in a child's literacy skills are followed through here with explanations of how help can be given. It includes a glossary of terms used in the literacy hour. 68-page pack written by Ruth Whiteley.

Winter Workshops ISBN 1 90530912 0; from 2007 978 1 90530912 2
Many worksheets giving templates and ideas for activities to use in workshops or as part of a course. 68-page pack written by Marion Gibbons.

Working Together ISBN 1 898614 69 5
Written to support the OCN Working Together course, which offers guidance to parents wishing to help in school. 52-page pack written by Cathy Lawes.

Writing ISBN 1 898614 70 9
3 sections giving: simple explanations on the five stages of writing, ie planning etc; how writing is put together to make sense, ie grammar etc; the various types of writing, ie forms etc 44-page pack written by Carol Gladstone.

Packs may be ordered from: avantibooks limited, The iO Centre, Unit 9 Whittle Way, Gunnels Wood Road, STEVENAGE, Hertfordshire, SG1 2BD
Tel: 01483 747000 Fax: 01438 741131
Email: enquiries@avantibooks.com Web: www.avantibooks.com